My Reward Chart

Praise and encourage your child with a daily star sticker and weekly reward sticker.

This week I will...	Monday	Tuesday	Wednesday	Thursday	Friday	Saturday	Sunday
1.							
2.							
3.							
4.							
5.							
6.							

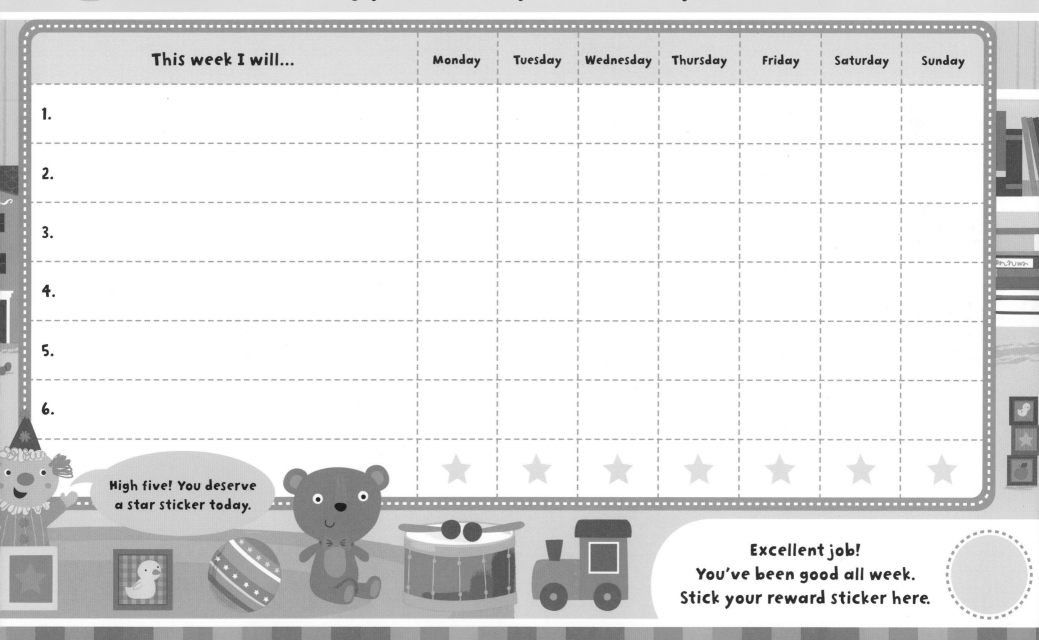

High five! You deserve a star sticker today.

Excellent job!
You've been good all week.
Stick your reward sticker here.

My Reward Chart

Praise and encourage your child with a daily star sticker and weekly reward sticker.

This week I will...	Monday	Tuesday	Wednesday	Thursday	Friday	Saturday	Sunday
1.							
2.							
3.							
4.							
5.							
6.							

You did it! You deserve a star sticker today.

Way to go!
You've worked hard all week.
Stick your reward sticker here.

My Reward Chart

Praise and encourage your child with a daily star sticker and weekly reward sticker.

This week I will...	Monday	Tuesday	Wednesday	Thursday	Friday	Saturday	Sunday
1.							
2.							
3.							
4.							
5.							
6.							

Good effort! You deserve a star sticker today.

Top marks!
You've been good all week.
Stick your reward sticker here.

My Reward Chart

Praise and encourage your child with a daily star sticker and weekly reward sticker.

This week I will...	Monday	Tuesday	Wednesday	Thursday	Friday	Saturday	Sunday
1.							
2.							
3.							
4.							
5.							
6.							

Great job! You deserve a star sticker today.

Well done!
You've worked hard all week.
Stick your reward sticker here.

My Reward Chart

Praise and encourage your child with a daily star sticker and weekly reward sticker.

This week I will...	Monday	Tuesday	Wednesday	Thursday	Friday	Saturday	Sunday
1.							
2.							
3.							
4.							
5.							
6.							

High five! You deserve a star sticker today.

Excellent job!
You've been good all week.
Stick your reward sticker here.

My Reward Chart

Praise and encourage your child with a daily star sticker and weekly reward sticker.

This week I will...	Monday	Tuesday	Wednesday	Thursday	Friday	Saturday	Sunday
1.							
2.							
3.							
4.							
5.							
6.							

You did it! You deserve a star sticker today.

Way to go!
You've worked hard all week.
Stick your reward sticker here.

My Reward Chart

Praise and encourage your child with a daily star sticker and weekly reward sticker.

This week I will...	Monday	Tuesday	Wednesday	Thursday	Friday	Saturday	Sunday
1.							
2.							
3.							
4.							
5.							
6.							

Good effort! You deserve a star sticker today.

Top marks!
You've been good all week.
Stick your reward sticker here.

My Reward Chart

Praise and encourage your child with a daily star sticker and weekly reward sticker.

This week I will...	Monday	Tuesday	Wednesday	Thursday	Friday	Saturday	Sunday
1.							
2.							
3.							
4.							
5.							
6.							

Great job! You deserve a star sticker today.

Well done!
You've worked hard all week.
Stick your reward sticker here.

My Reward Chart

This week I will...	Monday	Tuesday	Wednesday	Thursday	Friday	Saturday	Sunday
1.							
2.							
3.							
4.							
5.							
6.							

High five! You deserve a star sticker today.

Excellent job!
You've been good all week.
Stick your reward sticker here.

My Reward Chart

Praise and encourage your child with a daily star sticker and weekly reward sticker.

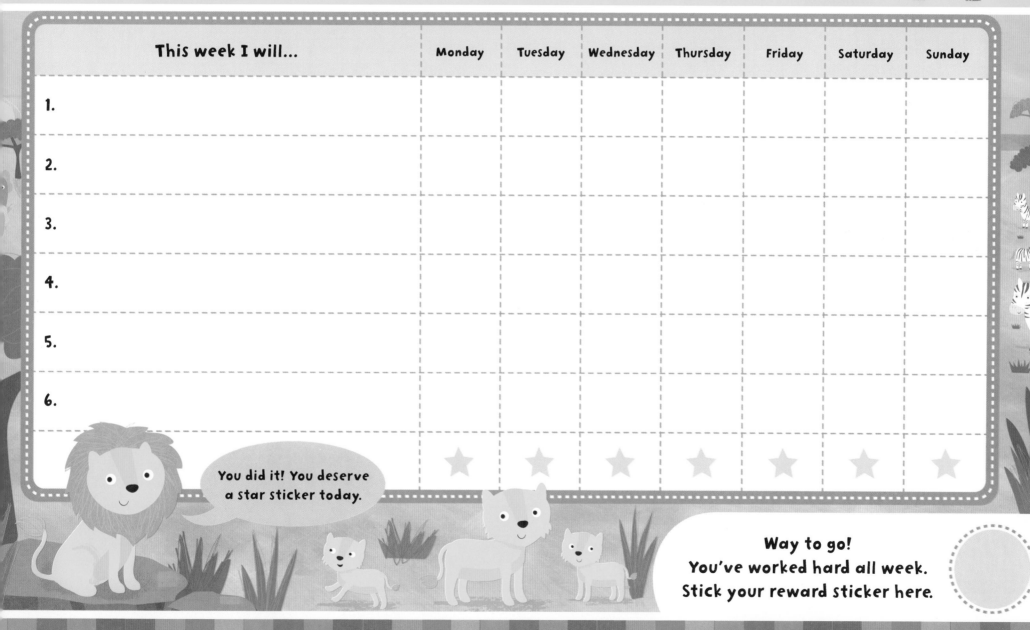

This week I will...	Monday	Tuesday	Wednesday	Thursday	Friday	Saturday	Sunday
1.							
2.							
3.							
4.							
5.							
6.							

You did it! You deserve a star sticker today.

Way to go!
You've worked hard all week.
Stick your reward sticker here.

My Reward Chart

Praise and encourage your child with a daily star sticker and weekly reward sticker.

This week I will...	Monday	Tuesday	Wednesday	Thursday	Friday	Saturday	Sunday
1.							
2.							
3.							
4.							
5.							
6.							

Good effort! You deserve a star sticker today.

Top marks!
You've been good all week.
Stick your reward sticker here.

My Reward Chart

This week I will...	Monday	Tuesday	Wednesday	Thursday	Friday	Saturday	Sunday
1.							
2.							
3.							
4.							
5.							
6.							

Great job! You deserve a star sticker today.

Well done!
You've worked hard all week.
Stick your reward sticker here.

My Reward Chart

This week I will...	Monday	Tuesday	Wednesday	Thursday	Friday	Saturday	Sunday
1.							
2.							
3.							
4.							
5.							
6.							

High five! You deserve a star sticker today.

Excellent job!
You've been good all week.
Stick your reward sticker here.

My Reward Chart

Praise and encourage your child with a daily star sticker and weekly reward sticker.

This week I will...	Monday	Tuesday	Wednesday	Thursday	Friday	Saturday	Sunday
1.							
2.							
3.							
4.							
5.							
6.							

You did it! You deserve a star sticker today.

Way to go!
You've worked hard all week.
Stick your reward sticker here.

My Reward Chart

Praise and encourage your child with a daily star sticker and weekly reward sticker.

This week I will...	Monday	Tuesday	Wednesday	Thursday	Friday	Saturday	Sunday
1.							
2.							
3.							
4.							
5.							
6.							
	★	★	★	★	★	★	★

Good effort! You deserve a star sticker today.

Top marks!
You've been good all week.
Stick your reward sticker here.

My Reward Chart

This week I will...	Monday	Tuesday	Wednesday	Thursday	Friday	Saturday	Sunday
1.							
2.							
3.							
4.							
5.							
6.							

Great job! You deserve a star sticker today.

Well done!
You've worked hard all week.
Stick your reward sticker here.

My Reward Chart

Praise and encourage your child with a daily star sticker and weekly reward sticker.

This week I will...	Monday	Tuesday	Wednesday	Thursday	Friday	Saturday	Sunday
1.							
2.							
3.							
4.							
5.							
6.	⭐	⭐	⭐	⭐	⭐	⭐	⭐

High five! You deserve a star sticker today.

Excellent job!
You've been good all week.
Stick your reward sticker here.

My Reward Chart

Praise and encourage your child with a daily star sticker and weekly reward sticker.

This week I will...	Monday	Tuesday	Wednesday	Thursday	Friday	Saturday	Sunday
1.							
2.							
3.							
4.							
5.							
6.							

You did it! You deserve a star sticker today.

Way to go!
You've worked hard all week.
Stick your reward sticker here.

My Reward Chart

Praise and encourage your child with a daily star sticker and weekly reward sticker.

This week I will...	Monday	Tuesday	Wednesday	Thursday	Friday	Saturday	Sunday
1.							
2.							
3.							
4.							
5.							
6.							

Good effort! You deserve a star sticker today.

Top marks!
You've been good all week.
Stick your reward sticker here.

My Reward Chart

Praise and encourage your child with a daily star sticker and weekly reward sticker.

This week I will...	Monday	Tuesday	Wednesday	Thursday	Friday	Saturday	Sunday
1.							
2.							
3.							
4.							
5.							
6.							

Great job! You deserve a star sticker today.

Well done!
You've worked hard all week.
Stick your reward sticker here.

My Reward Chart

Praise and encourage your child with a daily star sticker and weekly reward sticker.

This week I will...	Monday	Tuesday	Wednesday	Thursday	Friday	Saturday	Sunday
1.							
2.							
3.							
4.							
5.							
6.							

High five! You deserve a star sticker today.

Excellent job!
You've been good all week.
Stick your reward sticker here.

My Reward Chart

Praise and encourage your child with a daily star sticker and weekly reward sticker.

This week I will...	Monday	Tuesday	Wednesday	Thursday	Friday	Saturday	Sunday
1.							
2.							
3.							
4.							
5.							
6.							

You did it! You deserve a star sticker today.

Way to go!
You've worked hard all week.
Stick your reward sticker here.

My Reward Chart

Praise and encourage your child with a daily star sticker and weekly reward sticker.

This week I will...	Monday	Tuesday	Wednesday	Thursday	Friday	Saturday	Sunday
1.							
2.							
3.							
4.							
5.							
6.							

Good effort! You deserve a star sticker today.

Top marks!
You've been good all week.
Stick your reward sticker here.